Design drawing two

John Rolfe

icay

 HODDER AND STOUGHTON
LONDON SYDNEY AUCKLAND TORONTO

Preface

Together with Design Drawing One, this book presents a series of drawing examples based on the real and everyday world.

In Design Drawing Two, I have introduced several new areas of work, such as spirals, tangents and conic sections, and extended many of the areas started in Design Drawing One. However, the drawings from both books are linked by such topics as space, aircraft, cars, etc., in an attempt to stimulate the pupil's interest in looking for drawing examples of his own.

So many of the trappings of modern society start their life on a drawing board, and yet people usually take them for granted and look at them without really 'seeing' them or thinking about their origins. The examples in the book, therefore, are chosen to help the pupil observe the world around him, and to give him scope to develop his own ideas and designs (something which is often lacking in the more traditional approach towards Technical Drawing). I have also made an attempt to get the pupil to look at things closely by leaving a number of drawings in the book incomplete and asking the pupil to study the appropriate photographs carefully and add as much detail to his drawings as possible.

Most of the work in this book is based around traditional drawing skills and techniques, but the approach is such that I hope the pupil's interest is retained and his efforts steered towards observation and an appreciation of how it is possible to communicate graphically. Graphical communication is, after all, a universal language and one which is becoming increasingly important in an ever-shrinking world.

John Rolfe

ISBN 0 340 19258 5

First printed 1977

Reprinted 1979, 1981

Printed in Hong Kong for
Hodder and Stoughton Educational,
a division of Hodder and Stoughton Ltd.,
Mill Road, Dunton Green, Sevenoaks, Kent. TN13 2YD,
by Colorcraft Ltd.

Acknowledgements

The author and publisher would like to thank the following organisations who have allowed their trade or other marks to be used in this book, or who have supplied photographs. In all cases, the dimensions and methods of construction of the symbols are the responsibility of the author, and are not necessarily those employed by the organisations, whose co-operation in this respect is appreciated. Although care has been taken to make the proportions of drawings as accurate as possible, some simplification has been necessary in some cases.

Independent Television News (Exercise 1); English Electric Valve Co. Ltd. (2); A. H. McIntosh & Co. Ltd. (3); Phipps Photographic (4); The Joint Credit Card Co. Ltd. (5); Renault Ltd. (6); The Associated Press Ltd. (7, 27, 30, 31); The Peninsular and Oriental Steam Navigation Co. (8); John Mills Photography Ltd. (9); London Art Tech. (10); British Steel Corporation (11); Volvo Concessionaires Ltd. (12); James Neill (Sheffield) Ltd. (13); The Royal Bank of Scotland Ltd. (14); Richard Baker Advertising Ltd. (16); Lufthansa Photographic Service (17); Australian Information Service (18); British Airways (19); Simon Engineering (Dudley) Ltd. (20); Bison Garages Ltd. (21); RN Photo (22); Ministry of Defence, Crown Copyright (23, 46, 47, 51); F. W. Woolworth and Co. Ltd. (24); Fine Ltd. (25); The Esso Petroleum Co. Ltd. (26); Joseph Lucas Ltd. (28); Picturepoint Ltd. (29); Pye of Cambridge Ltd. (32); Keystone (33); G. Leslie Horn (34); British Domestic Appliances Ltd. (35); French Railways – Lafontant (36); British Leyland (37); Brian Long (38); Spiral Staircase Systems (39); Thorn Domestic Appliances Ltd. (40); Camera Press Ltd. (41); U.S.I.S. (42); Ford Motor Co. Ltd. (43); The British Petroleum Co. Ltd. (44, 56); The Cunard Steam Ship Co. Ltd. (45); Imperial War Museum, Crown Copyright (48, 52, 53); The British Hovercraft Corporation Ltd. (49); British Rail (50); Paul Popper Ltd. (54); Hawker Siddley (55).

1: Independent Television News

This example shows how letters can be linked
together to form a symbol.

a) Copy the drawing.

b) Using either your own initials or those of your
school or a football club see if you can
produce a similar sort of design by linking
the letters together in some way. Plan your
work carefully before you start on your
finished drawing.

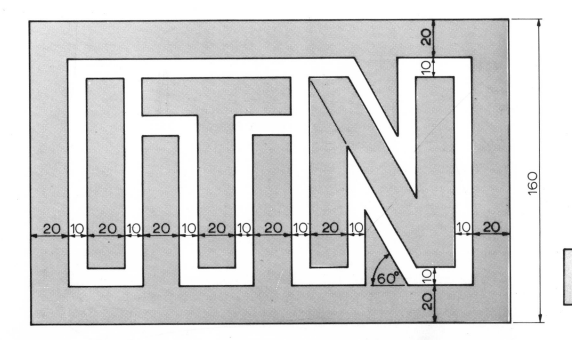

2: English Electric Valve Co. Ltd.

As with Example 1, this shows how two letters
can be linked together.

a) Make a drawing of this symbol.

b) See if you can design different ways of linking
   two letter E's together. Make an accurate
   drawing of your best design.

A3

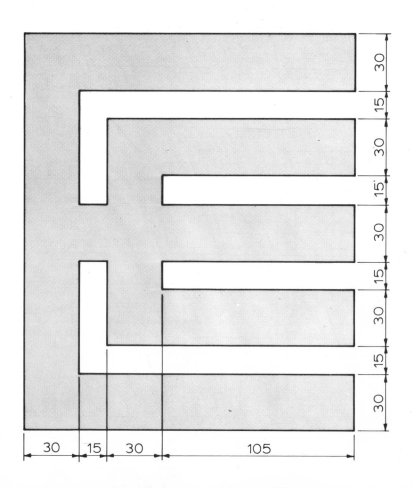

30
15
30
15
30
15
30
15
30

30 | 15 | 30 | 105

3: McIntosh Furniture

This very simple design shows a letter M. Using a square as the basis of your design see what other simple letters you can design. Make accurate drawings of three of your ideas.

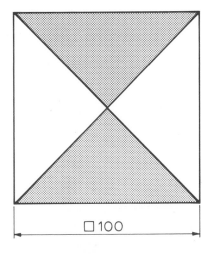

□100

A3

4: Yardley

Design a shape which would be suitable as a
background for the Yardley symbol. Make a
drawing of your design, including on it the
Yardley symbol.

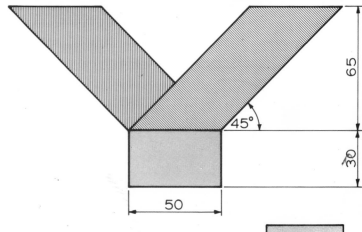

5: Access Card

Shown are details of how to draw the A on the
Access Card.

a) Given that the overall size of the card is
   370 mm $\times$ 240 mm, make an accurate
   drawing of the complete card.
b) Practice your lettering by putting on the
   information given on the card.

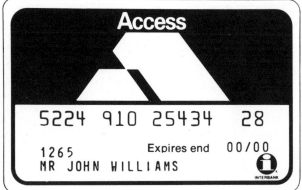

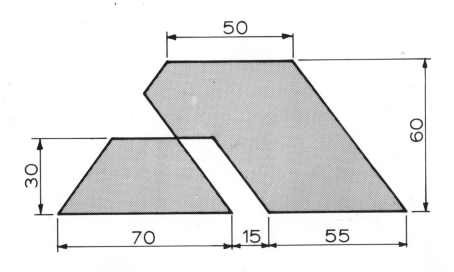

6: Renault

a) Draw the Renault badge to the sizes given.
b) Make, to a suitable scale, a separate drawing of the grill and headlamp arrangement of the Renault shown in the photograph. Do not include the badge on this drawing.

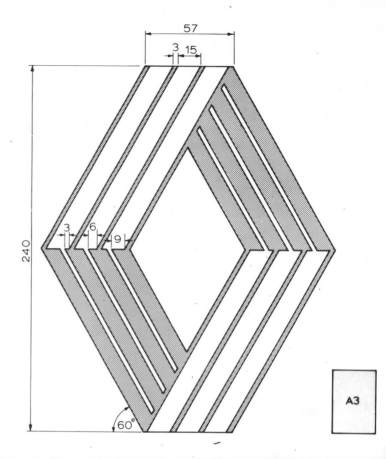

7: New Zealand Commonwealth Games

Here is the symbol used at the 1974 Commonwealth Games held in New Zealand.

a) Make a drawing of the symbol.
b) Find out where the next Commonwealth Games are to take place and design a symbol which could be used at those Games.

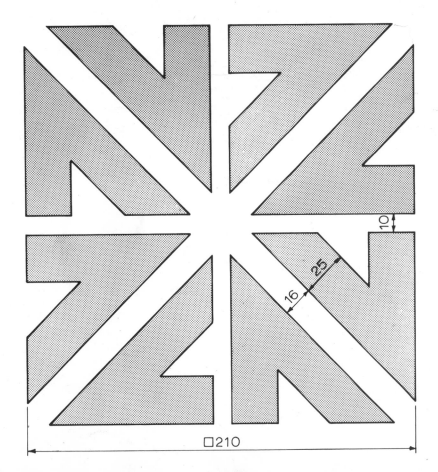

10

25

16

A3

□210

8: Ships' Code Flags

These drawings show the international code flags used by the world's shipping.
a) Study the photograph and see if you can discover the letters being sent in the signal.
b) Use this method of coding to draw your name.

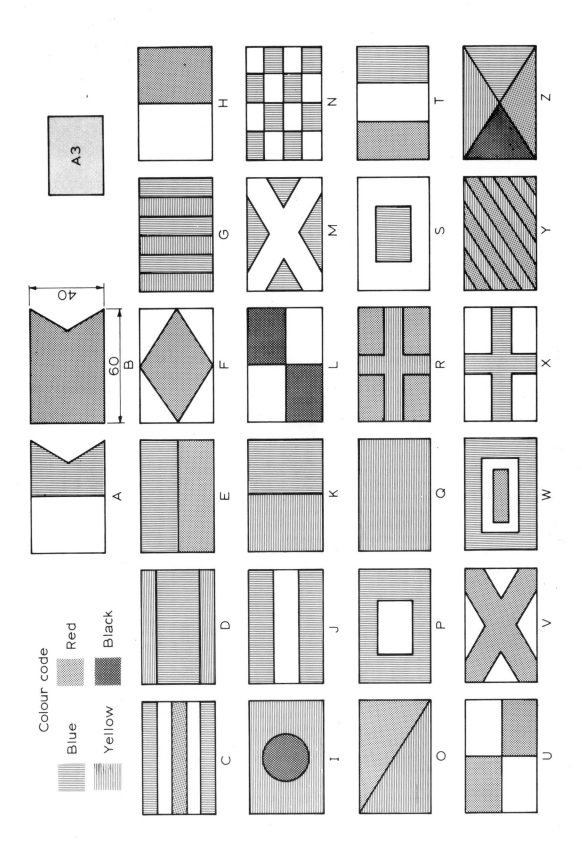

9: Liverpool R.C. Cathedral

You have here an incomplete drawing of Liverpool R.C. Cathedral.

a) Using this as the basis of your work, and the photograph for added information, make a detailed drawing of the Cathedral.

b) You could also try to make a model of the Cathedral. The basic building can be made from two cylinders and a truncated cone, with the various details being added later.

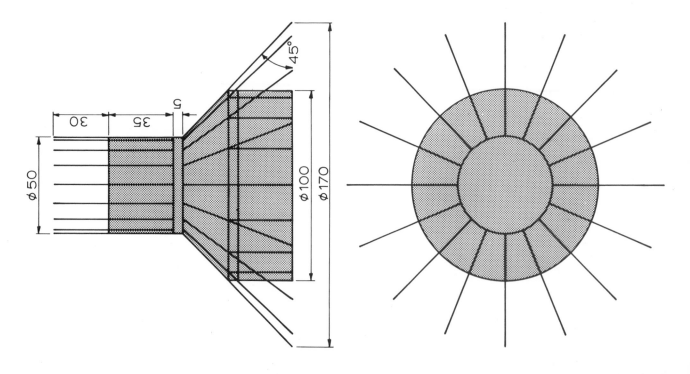

10: Indianapolis 500 Race Track

Where is this race track? See if you can find out any information about it.

The drawing shows a plan of the Indianapolis 500 Race Track. Copy the drawing but add to it a pits area which will allow the cars to pull off the track to undergo repairs and to refuel.

A3

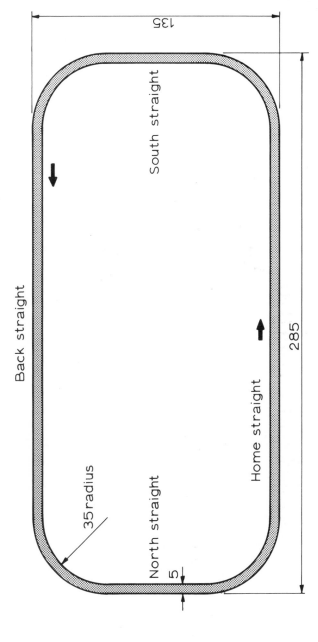

11: British Steel

a) Make a drawing of the British Steel symbol.
b) Now see if you can think of another design for
   a letter S and make an accurate drawing of
   your idea.

A3

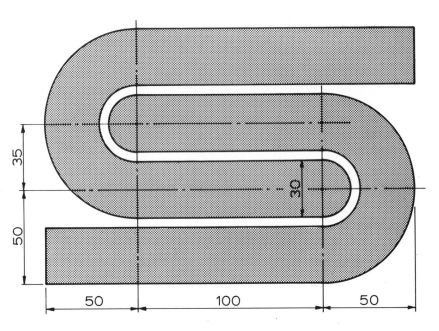

35

30

50

50   100   50

12: Volvo

The drawing shows the Volvo symbol. Design a
radiator grill for a Volvo which incorporates the
Volvo symbol. Use a scale of half full size for
your drawing.

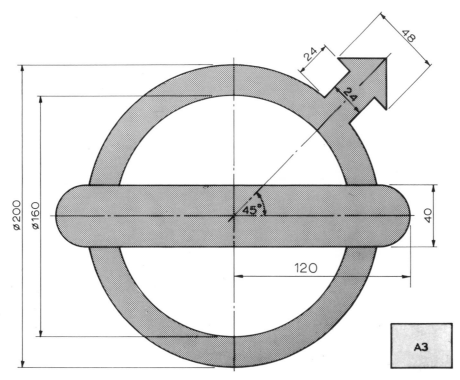

A3

13: Micrometer

a) Make a drawing of the micrometer shown.
b) See if you can find out what the different parts of a micrometer are called, and label your drawing.

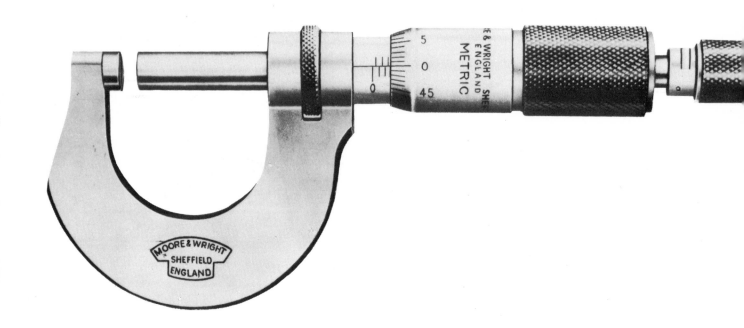

A3

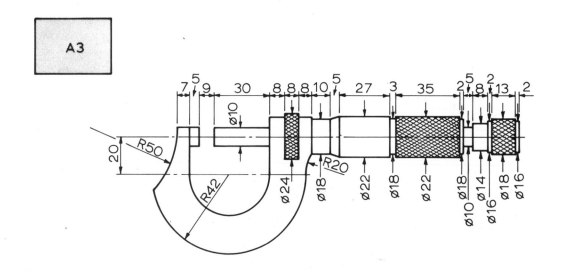

14: Royal Bank of Scotland

a) Make a drawing of the Royal Bank of Scotland symbol to the sizes given.

b) Design a suitable background shape on which the symbol could be mounted.

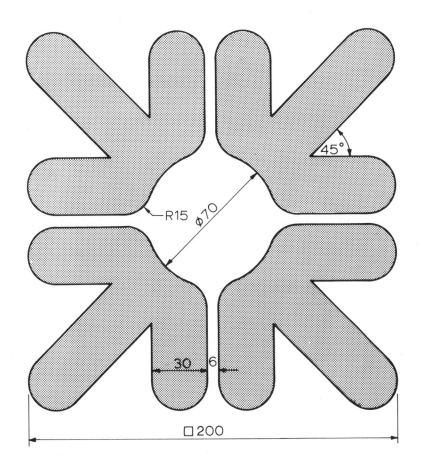

45°

R15 ⌀70

30 6

□200

A3

15: Montreal Olympic Games Symbol

Shown here are two postage stamps bearing the Montreal Olympic Games symbol of 1976. If you study it carefully, you will see it contains the five Olympic rings and a letter M.

a) Make a drawing of the symbol.

b) Find out where the next Olympic Games are going to take place and design a symbol for use at those Games.

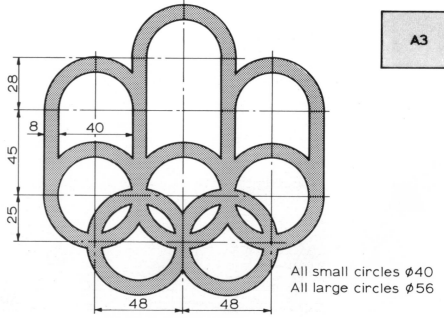

A3

All small circles ⌀40
All large circles ⌀56

16: Peter Dominic Wine Shops

A very clever design to suggest a bottle and two glasses is shown.

a) Make a drawing of this design.
b) Design and make an accurate drawing of a bottle different in shape to the one used in this symbol.

A3

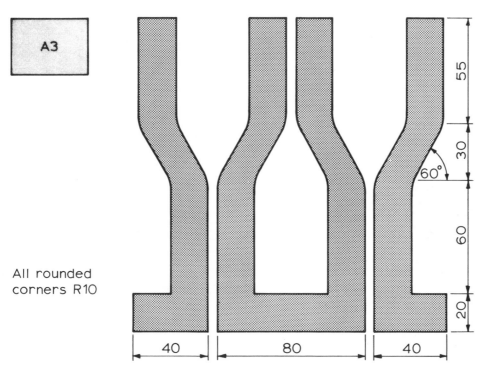

All rounded corners R10

55
30
60°
60
20

40
80
40

17: Jumbo Jet

Make a drawing of the Jumbo Jet using the sizes given. Study the photograph carefully and see what other details you can add to your drawing.

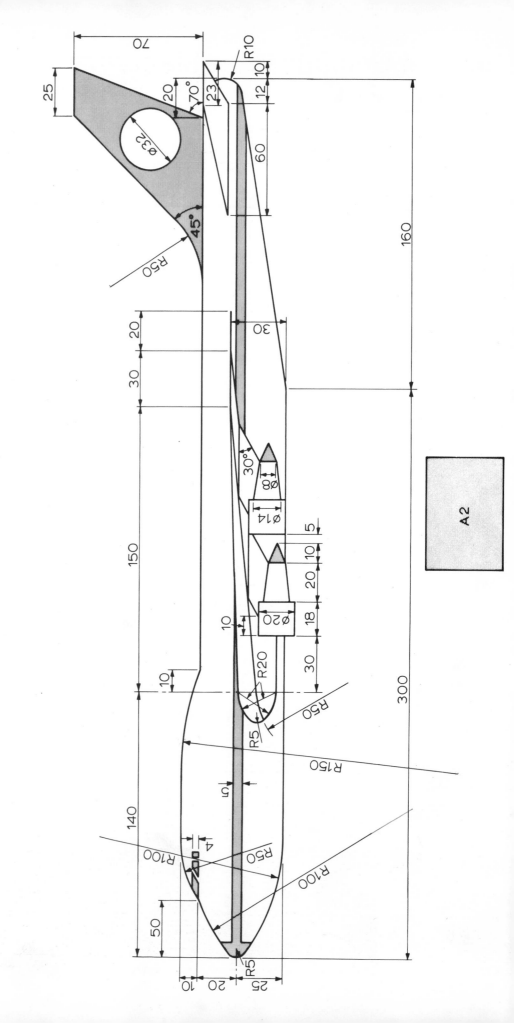

A2

18: Sydney Opera House

Shown is a photograph and an incomplete drawing of the Sydney Opera House. Using the information given, see if you can make a more detailed drawing of the Opera House.

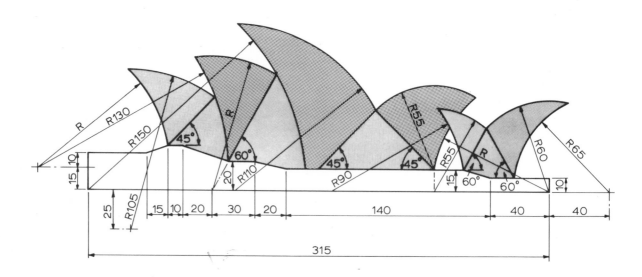

19: Aircraft Undercarriage

The drawing shows two views of part of an aircraft undercarriage in the down position. In the left hand view, one of the wheels has been removed to show the undercarriage mechanism more clearly. The points *A* and *B* on the undercarriage are fixed, but the points *C* and *D* hinge as indicated on the drawing as the undercarriage closes. Make a drawing of the undercarriage when it is in the closed position, i.e. the member *BC* is in the horizontal position.

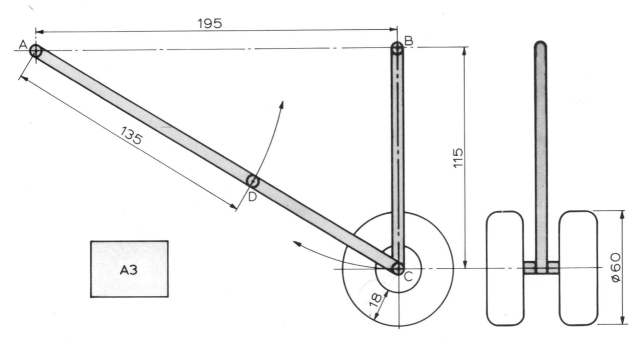

20: Hydraulic Lift

The drawing shows, in diagrammatic form, the mechanism of a hydraulic lift.

a) Draw the lift in its lowest position as shown in the drawing.

b) The platform of the lift rises in a vertical movement until it is in the second position shown in the drawing. When you have drawn the lift in this position, measure and state what angles X and Y are. The mechanism of the lift is free to pivot about points A, B and C.

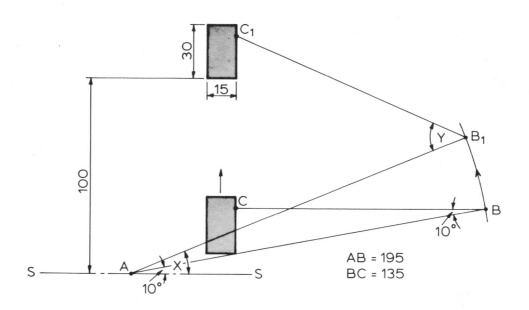

AB = 195
BC = 135

A3

21: Garage Door

The mechanism for an up-and-over garage door
is shown in diagrammatic form in the drawing.

a) Plot the locus of the bottom of the door from
the time it is fully closed until it is open and
in the horizontal position.

b) If the drawing were made to a scale of
50 mm to 1 metre, what would be the nearest
position to the door that a car could be parked
and still enable the garage to be opened?

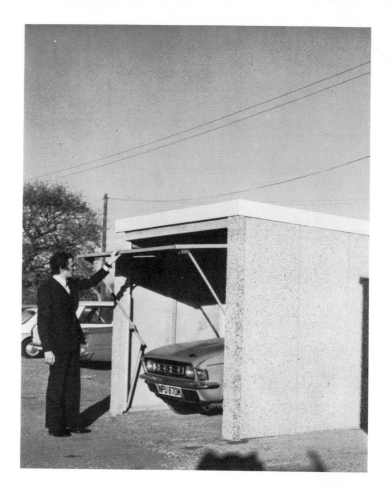

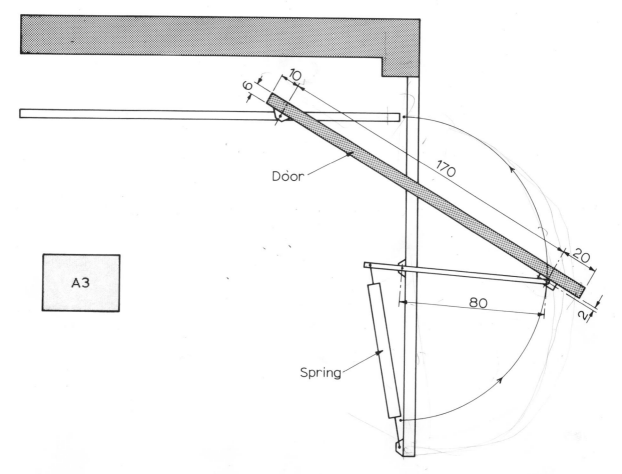

Door

170

10

6

20

80

2

Spring

A3

22: Minefield

A boat enters the mined area of a river, as
indicated in diagrammatic form in the drawing,
at point *A*. The only way that the boat can make
a safe journey through the minefield and exit at
point *B* is to plot a course such that the boat is
always an equal distance from each bank of the
river. Plot the course that the boat would have
to take.

A3

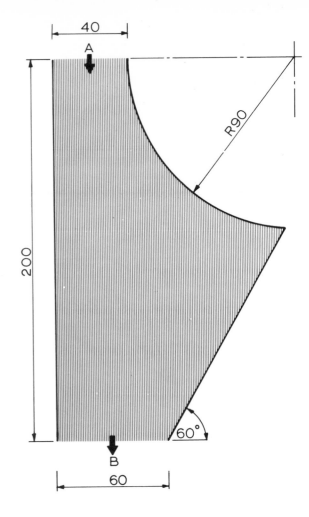

23: Aerobatics

The drawing shows part of the flight path of an aircraft during an aerobatic display.

When the aircraft is flying at a height of 3000 metres it makes a climb at an angle of 30° until it reaches a height of 11 000 metres, it then adopts a horizontal flight path and continues on this course for 9000 metres. The aircraft then dives in a semi-parabolic curve down to a height of 1000 metres. The vertex of the parabola indicates the bottom of the dive and the aircraft then adopts a horizontal flight path for another 6000 metres.

a) Using the information given in the above description and the drawing, make a drawing of the flight path of the aircraft. Use a scale of 10 mm to 1000 meters.

b) See if you can make up another aerobatic manœuvre and make a drawing of it. Then see if you can make a written description of the manœuvre.

A3

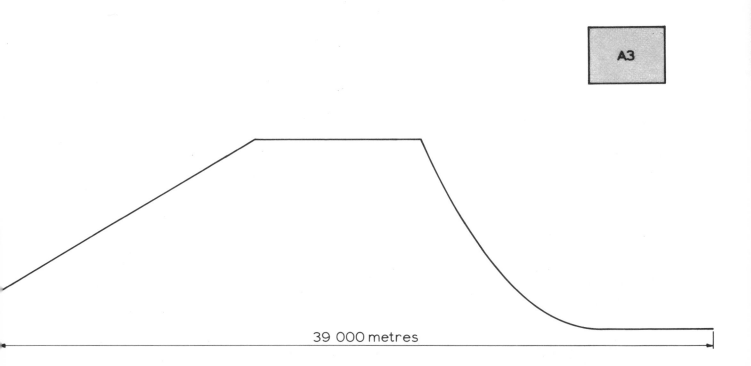

39 000 metres

24: Woolworth

The drawing shows the Winfield trade mark and is seen at all Woolworth stores. Six semi-ellipses have been linked together to form a letter W.

a) Make a drawing of this trade mark.

b) See if you can think of another letter which could be drawn using ellipses. Sketch out some ideas first of all and then make an accurate drawing of what you think to be your best idea.

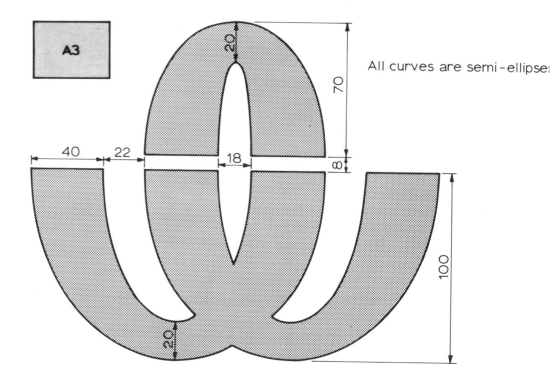

A3

All curves are semi-ellipses

25: Fine Fare

a) Make a drawing of the Fine Fare symbol.
b) Using a suitable scale, make a drawing of the
   lorry shown in the photograph.

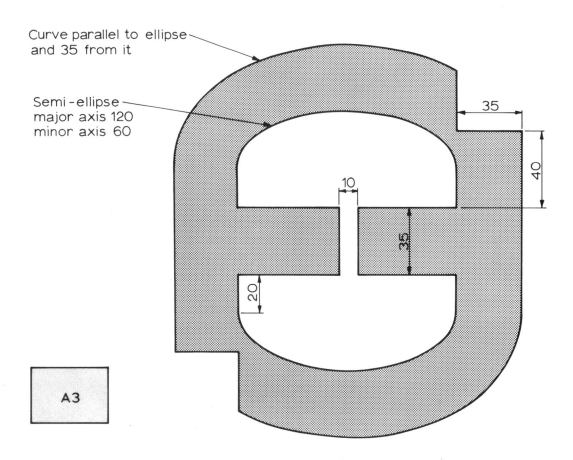

Curve parallel to ellipse
and 35 from it

Semi-ellipse
major axis 120
minor axis 60

35

40

10

35

20

A3

26: Esso

Details are given to enable you to draw the Esso symbol. Using this information make a complete drawing of the back of one of the tankers shown in the photograph.

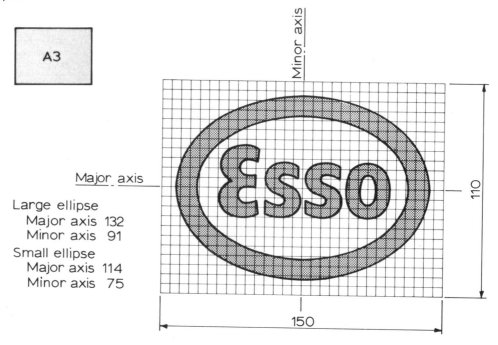

A3

Minor axis

Major axis

Large ellipse
 Major axis 132
 Minor axis 91
Small ellipse
 Major axis 114
 Minor axis 75

110

150

27: Radio Telescope

a) Draw the given view of the radio telescope.
b) The dish of the telescope is tilted so that the front surface is at an angle of 60° to the ground. With the dish in this new position draw an elevation of the dish similar to that in the first part of the question, and an end elevation in the direction of the arrow.

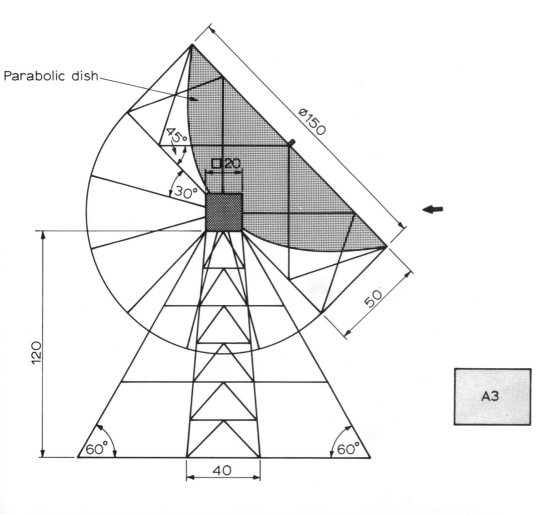

Parabolic dish

45°

⌀150

□20

30°

50

120

60°   60°

40

A3

28: Car Headlamp

The reflector on most car headlamps is parabolic in shape, do you know why?

a) Draw a section through a car headlamp to the sizes given in the drawing.

b) Design a layout for the following lights on the front of a car: twin headlamps, side lights, and direction indicators. Make an accurate drawing of your design.

A3

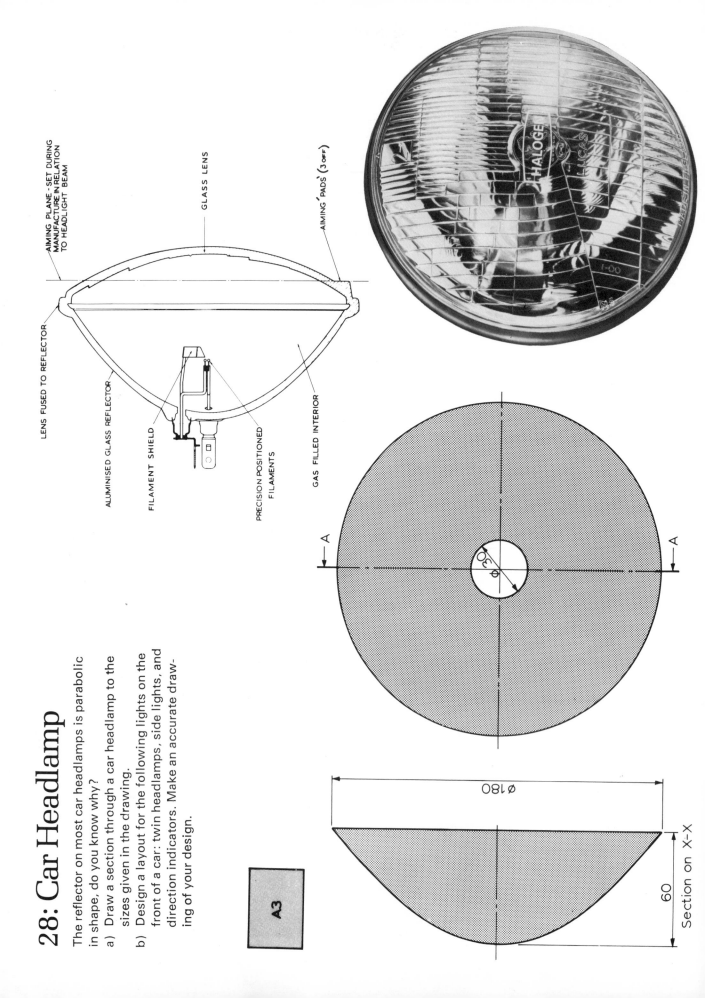

AIMING PLANE - SET DURING MANUFACTURE IN RELATION TO HEADLIGHT BEAM

GLASS LENS

AIMING 'PADS' (3 OFF)

LENS FUSED TO REFLECTOR

ALUMINISED GLASS REFLECTOR

FILAMENT SHIELD

PRECISION POSITIONED FILAMENTS

GAS FILLED INTERIOR

Ø30

Ø180

60

Section on X-X

29: Gateway Arch

Shown here is the Gateway Arch at St. Louis, Missouri, in the United States of America. The arch consists of two parabolic curves. Make a drawing of the arch to the sizes given.

A3

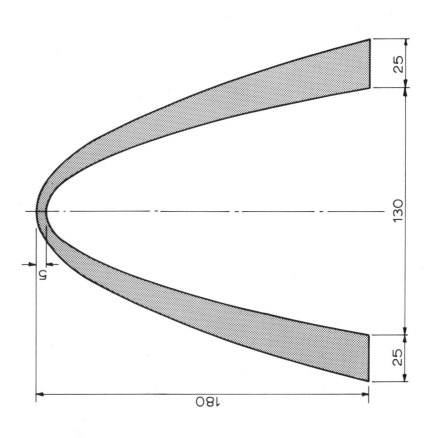

30: Path of a Cricket Ball

A fielder standing 30 metres from the wicket
throws a cricket ball and hits the stumps. The
ball travels in a parabolic curve reaching a
maximum height of 12 metres. Draw, to a suitable
scale, the path of the cricket ball.

31: Forth Road Bridge

Shown are a photograph and two drawings of the
Forth Road Bridge.
a) Draw the side view of the bridge using the
given information.
b) The main dimensions of the cross section of
the bridge are given. Choose a suitable scale,
and, using your own judgement for sizes not
given, make a detailed cross-sectional drawing
of the bridge.

A3

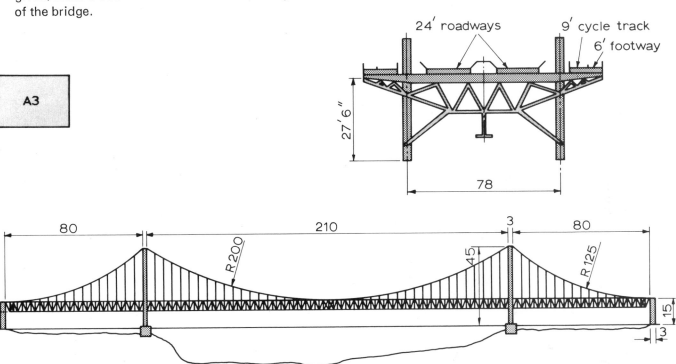

24' roadways   9' cycle track   6' footway

27' 6"

78

80   210   3   80

R200   45   R125

5   15   3

32: Pye

The Pye symbol consists of three letters drawn in isometric projection contained in a circle.
a) Make a drawing of the symbol.
b) Using the same technique draw your own initials in isometric projection in a circle or other suitable shape. Plan your work well before you start your final drawing.

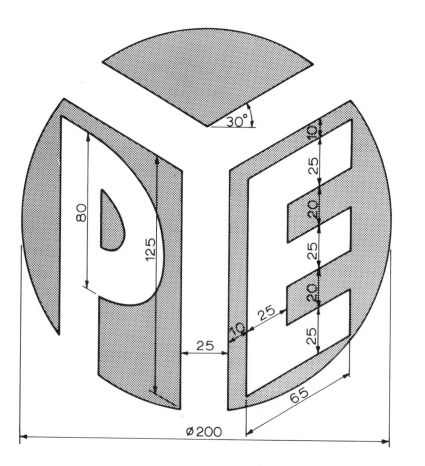

33: Hot Air Balloon

a) Draw the given view of a hot-air balloon,
   making sure that the tangents are constructed
   accurately.
b) See what other types of balloon you can find
   out about, and make a drawing of one of these.

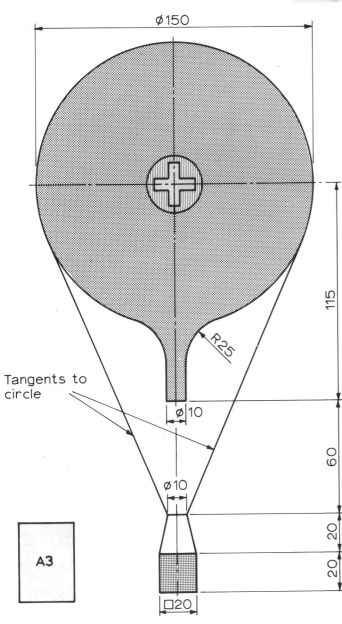

Tangents to circle

A3

Ø150

115

R25

Ø10

60

Ø10

20

20

□20

34: Bentley

The drawing shows an incomplete view of the Bentley shown in the photograph. Copy this drawing and see what other details you can add to it by studying the photograph.

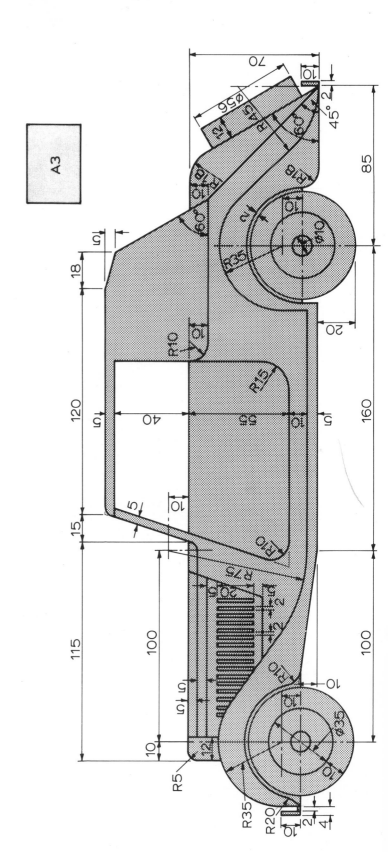

A3

35: Box Design

The overall sizes of the electric iron shown in the photograph are 240 mm long, 125 mm wide and 150 mm high. Design a box which could be made in cardboard to hold the electric iron. The box is to be made in two parts: a main box, and a separate lid which slides over the box. Your design should include any flaps necessary to join the other box together.

Choose a suitable scale and draw the developments necessary to make your box design. Try to show which parts are flaps and where the cardboard would have to be folded.

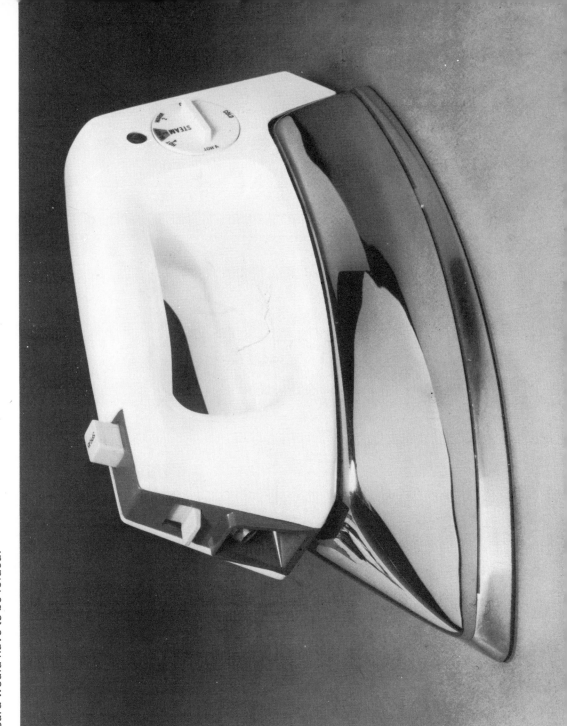

36: Steam Train

The drawing shows details of the funnel and part
of the boiler of a steam train. Draw these two
views, taking care to construct the line of intersection between the boiler and the funnel.

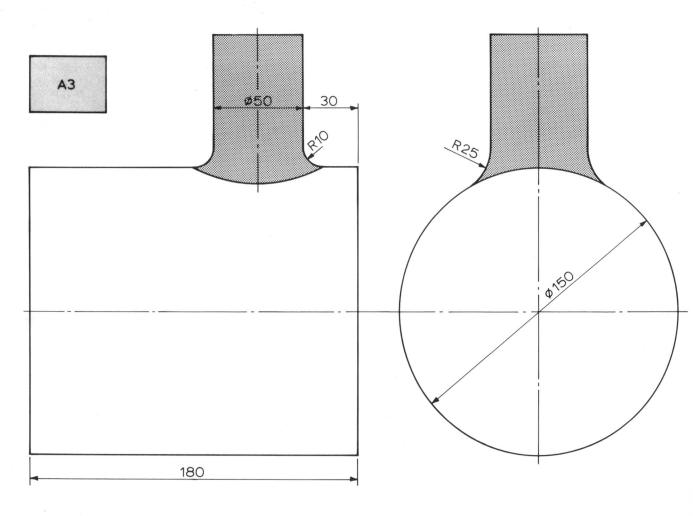

A3

Ø50

30

R10

180

R25

Ø150

37: Air Filter

The air filter shown here would be made in separate pieces. How would they be joined together?

Draw the two given views, making sure you plot the line of intersection carefully.

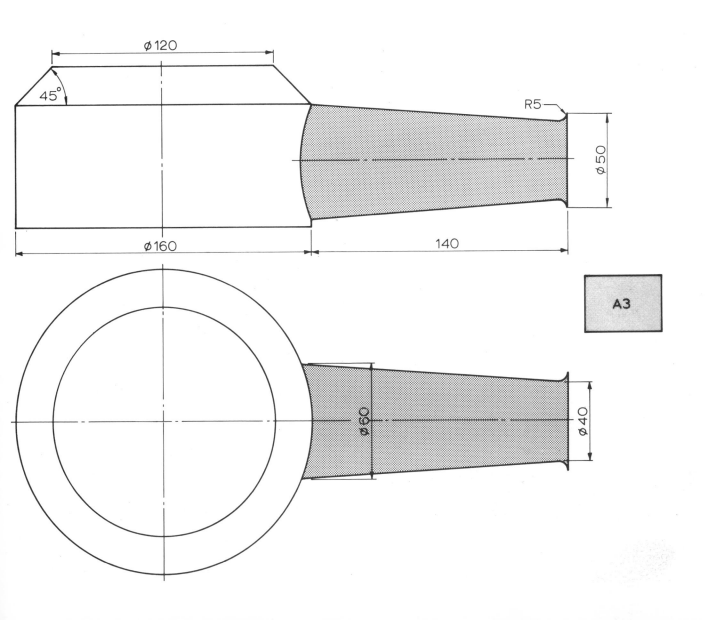

38: Optical illusions

The drawings shown here are drawn in either isometric or oblique projection. Which are which?

a) Make accurate drawings of the examples shown here.

b) Can you think of any other optical illusions? See if you can make drawings of other examples.

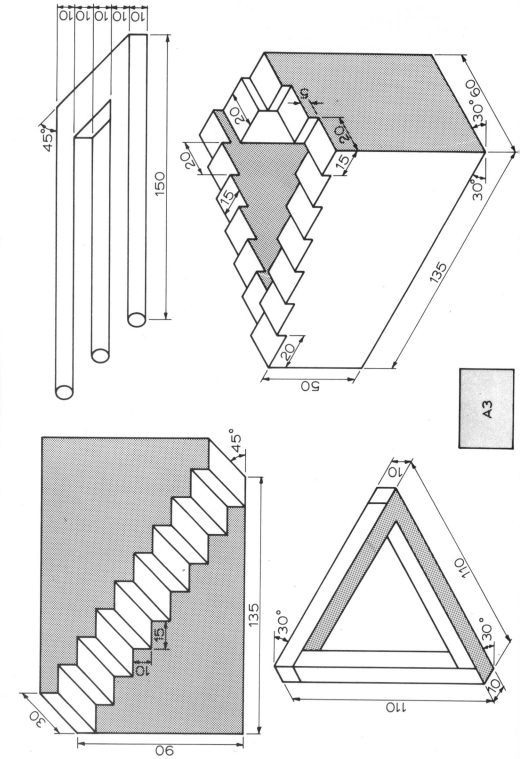

39: Spiral Staircase

The handrail on this staircase is in the form of a helix.

a) Make a drawing of the part of the staircase shown in the drawing.

b) Can you think of any other places where a helix occurs? Try to make a drawing of another example.

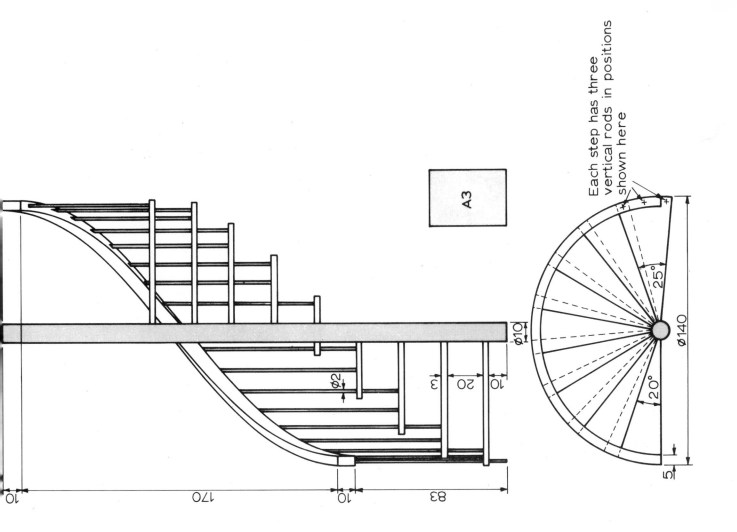

Each step has three vertical rods in positions shown here

40: Spiral Hotplate

The spiral on this hotplate has been drawn in the
form of an Archimedian spiral. Make a drawing of
the spiral, adding any other detail you can obtain
from the photograph.

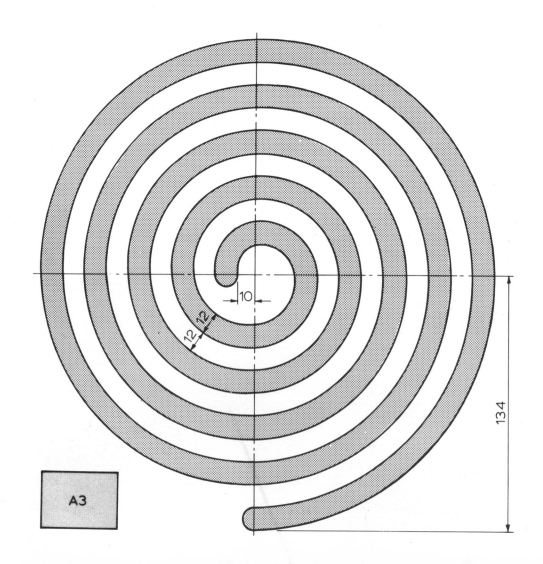

41: Helter-skelter

The drawing here is based on a conical spiral.
Make a drawing of the helter-skelter, adding any
other detail you can obtain from the photograph.

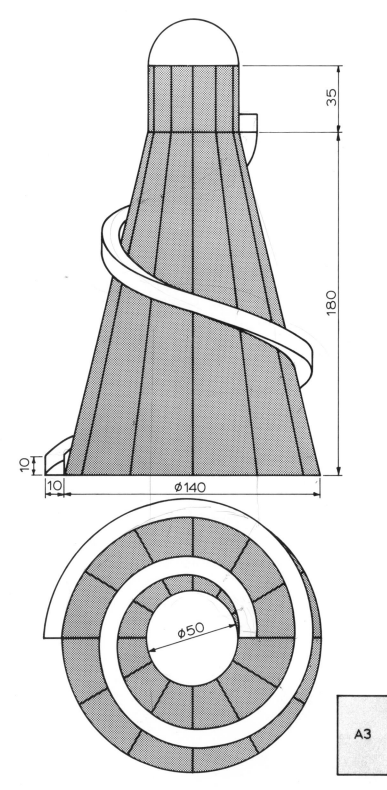

42: Saturn V Rocket

Shown are the various stages which go together
to make up the Saturn V Rocket and Apollo
Spacecraft. Make a drawing of the assembled
Rocket and Spacecraft.

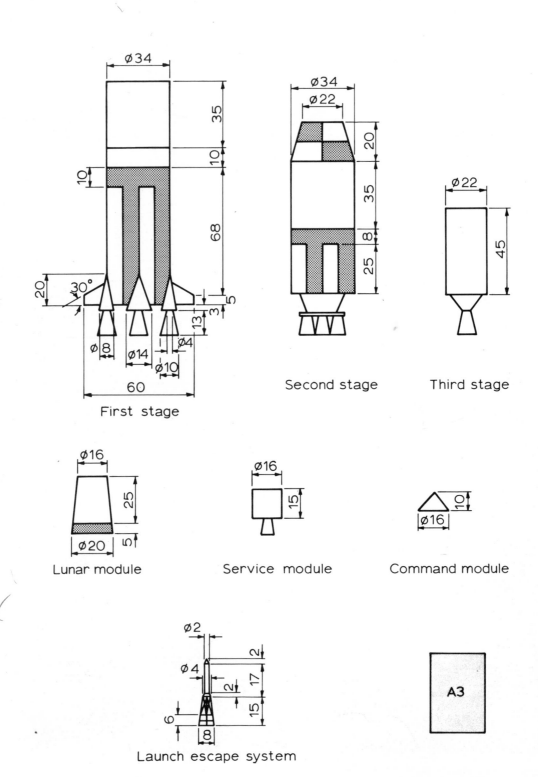

First stage

Second stage

Third stage

Lunar module

Service module

Command module

Launch escape system

A3

43: Model T Ford

The drawing shows an incomplete view of the Model T Ford shown in the photograph. Copy this drawing and see what other details you can add to it by studying the photograph.

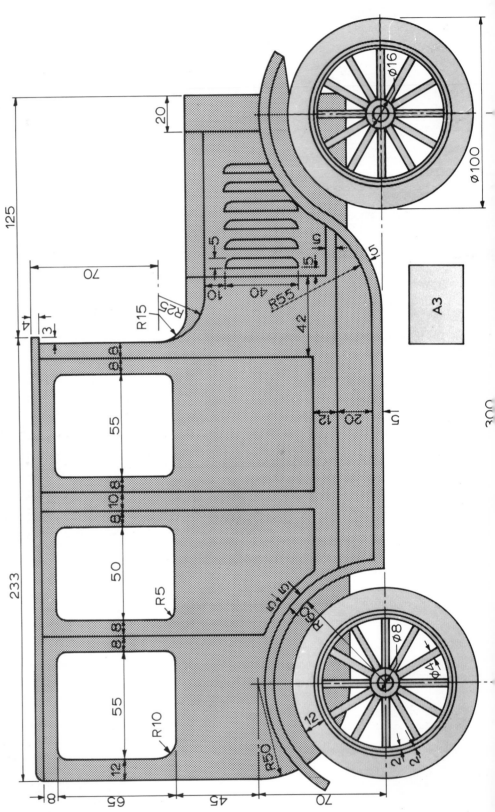

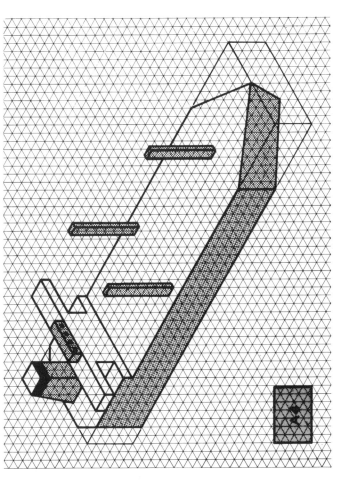

44: Oil Tanker

Using a piece of A4 paper ruled with 5 mm squares, draw a front elevation, an end elevation and a plan of the oil tanker. Count the squares from the isometric grid to obtain the sizes for your drawing.

45: Ocean Liner

The drawing here shows two views of the Queen
Elizabeth 2. Draw these two views on 5 mm
squared paper. Try to improve your drawing by
adding any other details you can obtain by studying the photograph.

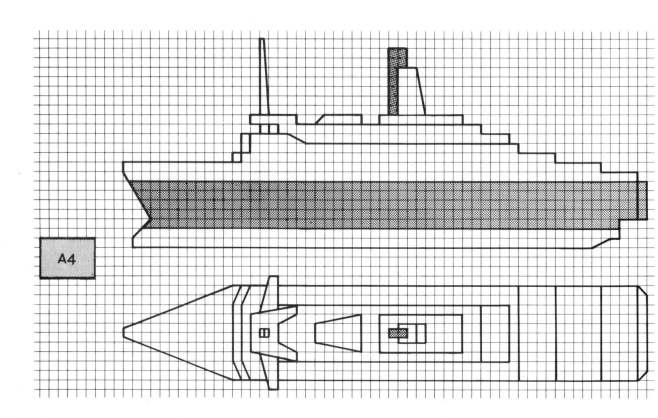

A4

46: Aircraft Carrier

Using the same technique as in Example 44, draw
the front elevation, plan and end elevation of the
aircraft carrier. The deck and superstructure
should be joined with the hull in your drawing.

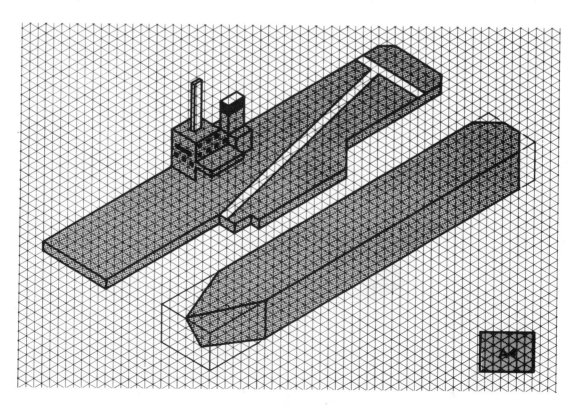

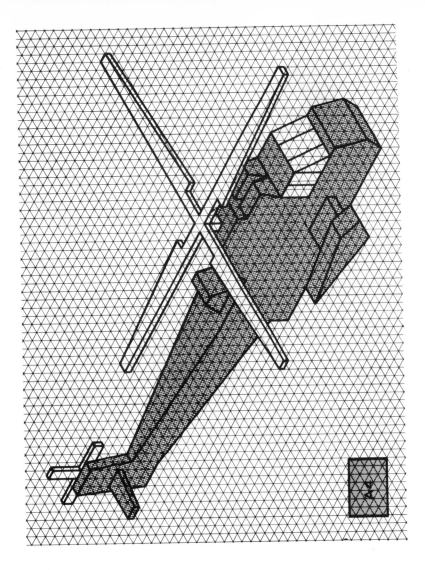

47: Helicopter

Draw a front elevation, plan and end elevation of the helicopter using the same technique as in Examples 44 and 45.

Note: *You will not be able to fit in all of the rotor blades in the end elevation and plan.*

48: V1 Rocket

The drawing shows two views of a V1 Rocket.
Draw these two views and, by studying them and
the photograph, add a plan view to your drawing.

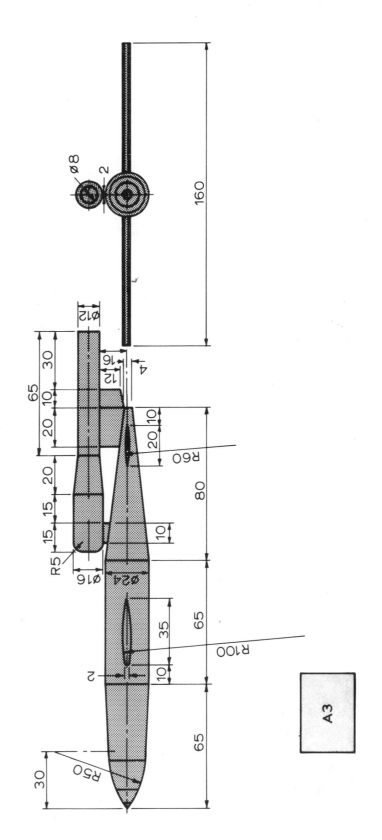

A3

49: Hovercraft

The drawing shows two views of a hovercraft.
Draw these two views, and by studying them and
the photographs add a plan view to your
drawing.

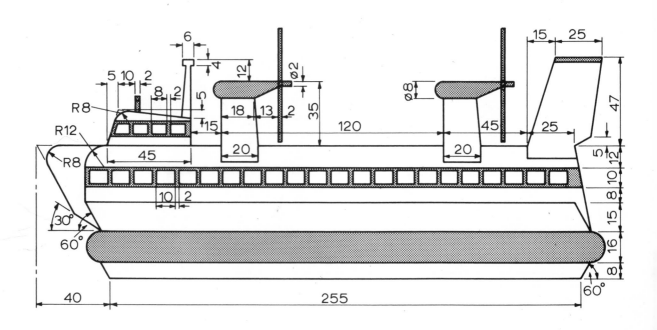

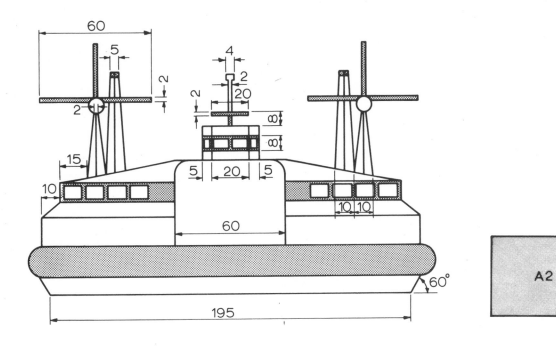

50: Cross Channel Ferry

Draw the two given views of a cross channel
ferry, adding any extra detail you can obtain
from the photograph. Then draw an end elevation
looking on to the front of the boat.

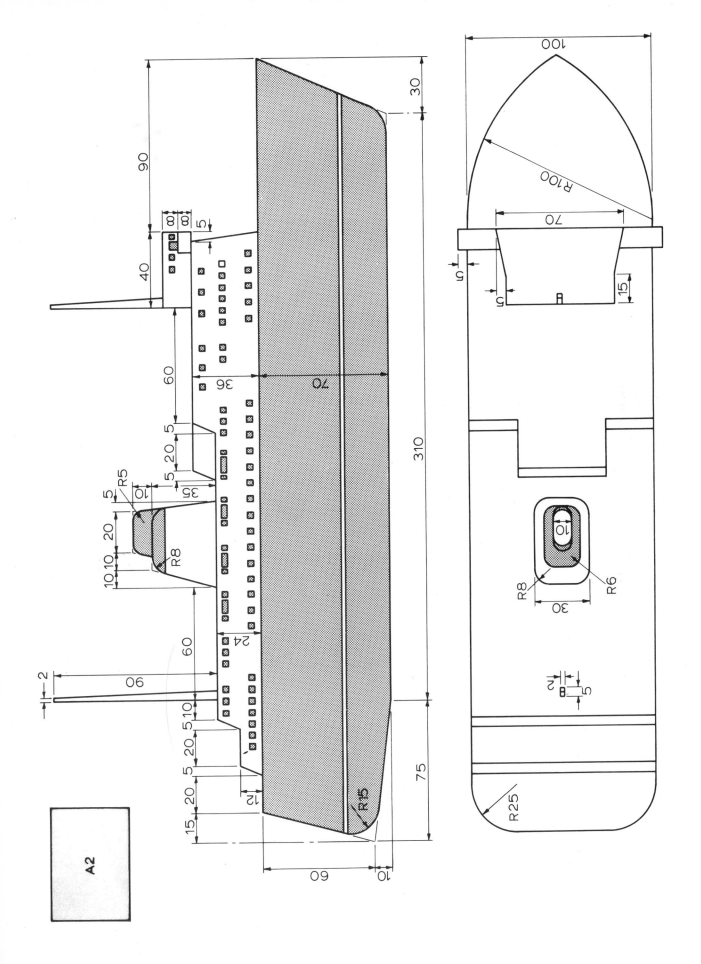

51: Submarine

Draw the given views of the submarine.

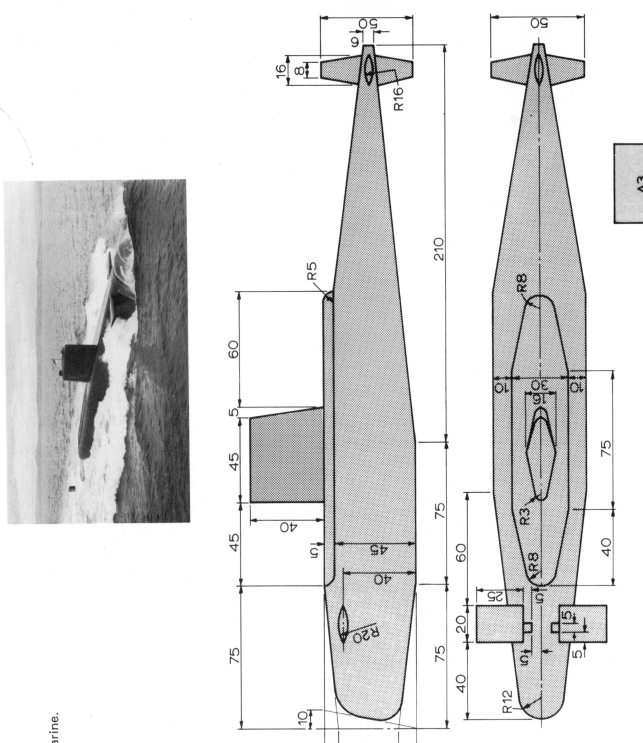

52: World War 1 Tank

The drawing shows two views of a Mark V Male Tank. Draw these two views and, by studying them and the photograph, add an end elevation to your drawing.

A3

53: Modern Tank

Draw the two given views of a tank and add an end elevation looking at the front of the tank.

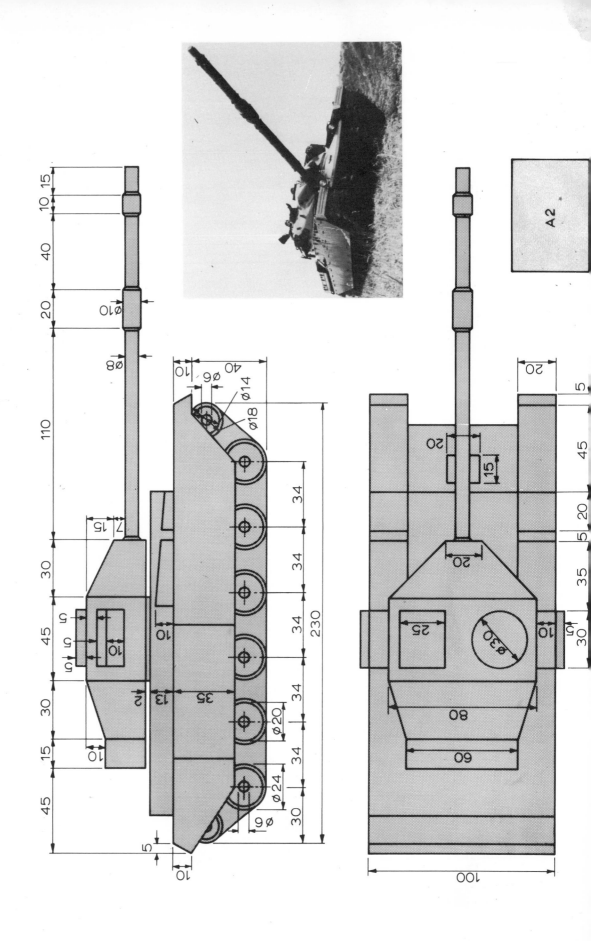

A2

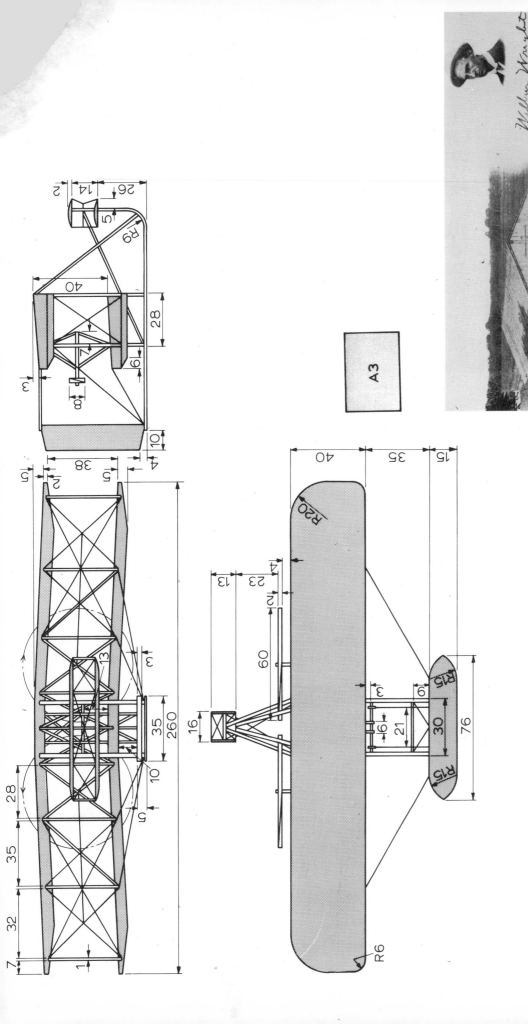

54: Wright Brothers' Flyer

Draw the given views of the Wright Brothers' Flyer.

A3

55: Hawker Harrier Jump Jet

Draw the given views of a Hawker Harrier.
Perhaps by studying the photographs you can add
a few more details to your drawing.

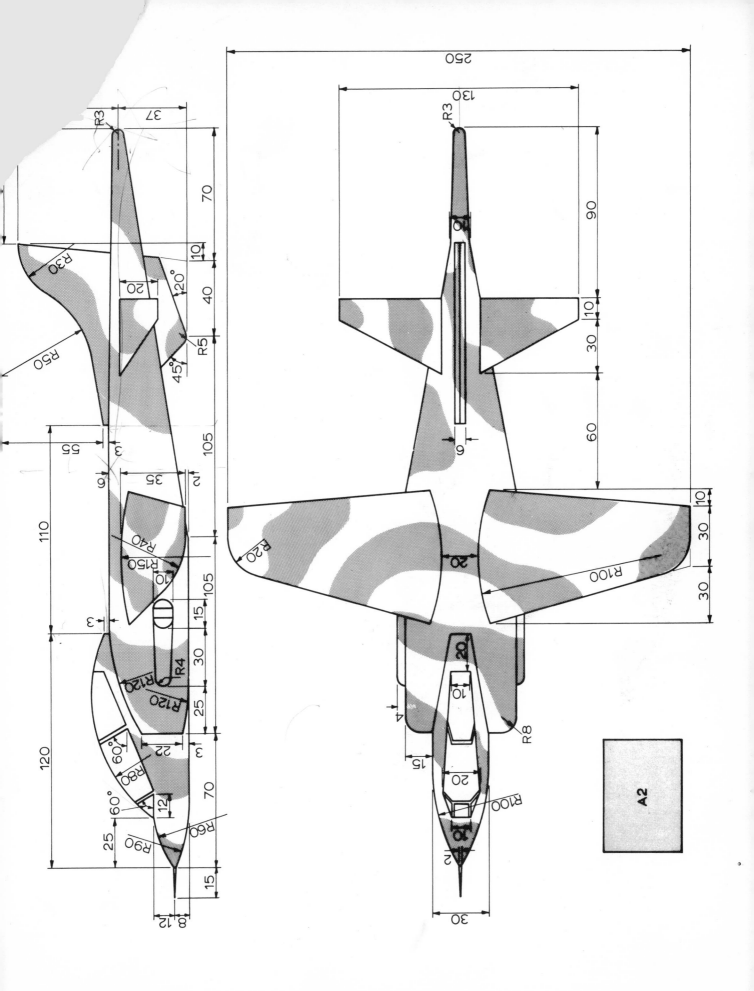

A2

56: North Sea Oil Rig

The drawing shows the platform of a North Sea oil rig. Using this as a basis of your work, make a drawing of an oil rig, complete with super-structure, as shown in the photograph. Add as much detail as you can by carefully studying the photograph.

A2

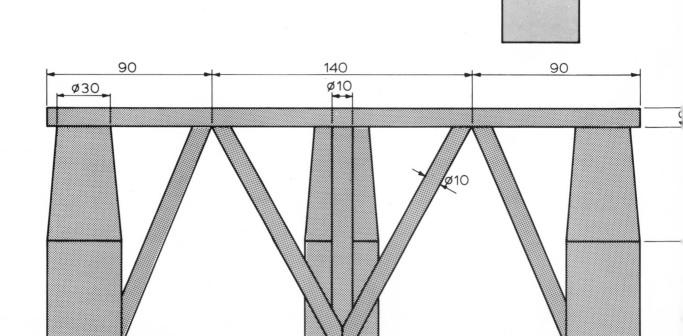